St. Tiggy

Wildlife Hospital

Wilf, the Smallest Badger
in the World
and other stories

First published in Great Britain
by Collins in 1998

1 3 5 7 9 8 6 4 2

Collins is an imprint of HarperCollins*Publishers* Ltd,
77 - 85 Fulham Palace Road, Hammersmith, London W6 8JB

Printed and bound in Great Britain
by Caledonian International Book Manufacturing Ltd,
Glasgow, G64

ISBN 0 00 675299 3

ST. TIGGYWINKLES WILDLIFE HOSPITAL

Wilf, the Smallest Badger
in the World
and other stories

Les Stocker

Collins
An Imprint of HarperCollins*Publishers*

Contents

Introduction

For twenty years Sue, Colin and I have been taking in wild animals and birds that have been injured. The stories in this book tell of just a few of these amongst the thousands we have been privileged to meet, treat and release. It is a great pity we cannot let anybody into St. Tiggywinkles to meet our patients, for these animals are either too wild, nervous or sick to be disturbed. But we want to meet you and show you the work we are doing, so we have built a Visitor Centre which shows the story of St. Tiggywinkles, without disturbing the sick animals and birds.

I hope these stories tell you something of the wonderful animals Britain has and that you manage to come and meet some of us at the St. Tiggywinkles Visitor Centre and National Hedgehog Sanctuary.

People at St. Tiggywinkles

**Les, Sue and
Colin Stocker**   Founders and Directors

Dr John Lewis   Specialist veterinary
                                   consultant

Lisa Frost   Head of Animal Services

Verity Sewell-Rutter   Visitor Centre organiser

Andrea Sims   Runs the office and
                                   always types my books!

**Plus over a hundred support staff, veterinary nurses
and volunteers**

Sulky, Silky and Tom

St. Tiggywinkles is a hospital for wild animals and birds. It's in the countryside not far from London. Just like hospitals for people, our patients arrive for treatment at all times of the day and night, and we pride ourselves on being able to give the best possible care to any species of wild bird or animal that needs our help.

One bitterly cold January night a giant furniture lorry arrived at St. Tiggwinkles. We were tired and cold as we stood there shivering, wondering what was waiting for us behind the big, black back doors of the lorry.

David Emmett, the driver of the lorry, climbed wearily from his cab and went round to the back of the truck to unlock the doors. He had phoned us just twenty-four hours earlier, to say that about sixty birds and animals were in desperate need of help. At the moment they were being cared for in the garden of a house in Norfolk, but that was going to come to an end the following week. He offered to bring the animals down to us if we were willing to look after them. Of course we said yes!

David now smiled cheerfully at us, making it hard to imagine that he'd just driven a hundred-and-fifty miles from Norfolk. He'd had to stop every hour, too, and make sure his precious cargo of animals was watered and comfortable.

All that day, we had moved our hedgehogs

out of their room into three others, and had set about building some more wooden pens to house the new patients.

Now, as David opened the doors, we were all a little worried about what we were going to see. But it didn't take us long to realise that we had made the right decision when we saw the row of big sad eyes looking out at us from the gloomy interior of the lorry.

Lined up across the back of the truck were four low, wire cages. Out of each one gazed several pairs of big, sad brown eyes and they seemed to be looking at us and asking, "Where are we now?"

I wanted to tell them not to worry and that they were in safe hands, but of course they couldn't understand. The eyes we first saw belonged to four young seals who needed looking after until they were big enough to go back to their home in the cold North Sea.

Also on the lorry were dozens of seabirds, gannets and divers, some little penguins, guillemots and razorbills. As we started to unload them into their new pens, we noticed that they had travelled well, and looked quite bright-eyed and alert.

The birds were easy to move but the seals, even though they were young, were heavy and took a lot of lifting. One of them, Crockett, was a grey seal, and it took two people to lift his cage. But the other three were common seals and weren't quite as heavy.

We couldn't carry Crockett through the hedgehog room door so David, who'd got to know him quite well, opened his cage and waved a fish in front of his nose. Out he came, flop, flop, flop, following David, who led him right into his new pen – easy!

Two of the other seals, who'd been named

Silky and Tom, slid into their new pens without any problem, but the other one, Sulky, didn't want to go, and started biting everything in sight. First his cage, then its door, then the door of the pen, the water dish and even one of our helper's wellies, all ended up with teeth marks to show that Sulky had arrived! It was chaos, with all of us jumping out of his way as he managed to push open the door of his cage and flop towards some of the bird pens. Thinking quickly, I grabbed a piece of board and managed to push him back in, slamming the wire door behind him. As quick as a flash, he slid round and lunged at me, as if to say "I'll get you in the end!"

"Not if I can help it," I thought to myself, staring at his mouthful of enormous teeth which gleamed at me through the cage.

Later, when all the birds and animals were in their pens, we set about giving them a good fish supper. The birds were easy enough and so was Crockett, the grey seal, but the three other seals were too young to feed themselves, and it meant one of us would have to go in and feed them all by hand.

I decided to volunteer Lisa, our animal carer, for the job. But I did stand outside the pens and offer my encouragement. Lisa has a knack with young animals which, in a situation like this, might just make the difference between co-operation and all-out war.

To hand-feed a young seal, the first thing you have to do is slide a piece of hard plastic tube over the index finger of your left hand. Then you go into the pen, throw a towel over the seal's head, and try to sit astride its shoulders, holding its head straight out in front, so that it can't turn and bite you. Then you take the towel off its head and – wait for it – stick your finger, covered with the plastic tube, into its mouth. Then of course it bites on the finger but can't close its jaws. With the other hand, you quickly push a fish, head first, into the other side of its mouth, until it swallows it. Then, when it won't take any more fish, you jump off the seal and get out of the pen as fast as you can!

Now you can see why I thought Lisa should do the first feed... As always, she made it look very easy and even managed to get five slippery herrings into Sulky, the last one to be fed.

But more problems were to come. Dr John, our consultant vet, had to give the seals a thorough examination. They all seemed fine, all that is except Sulky. We knew he'd got some ulcers on his skin that would need treatment, but Dr John also said that he was suffering from pneumonia and would need medicine every day for the next few weeks.

We could put tablets in Sulky's fish, but the ulcers would need to have ointment on them, and he certainly wouldn't like that very much.

Over the next few weeks, while the ulcers were being treated, Sulky managed to destroy three brooms, one hosepipe, a pair of Wellies, and goodness knows how many sets of hinges, which he wrenched off the door of his pen. At last his ulcers healed, and Dr John was happy that the pneumonia had cleared up too.

As Sulky got better, he got bigger and bigger, and harder and harder to handle. He still hadn't learnt to feed himself and if we went on like this, I was sure he would soon be adding somebody's finger to his menu! It was then I decided to put Sulky, Silky and Tom into an outside pool.

In the pool, Sulky wouldn't be fed by us any more, so he'd soon begin to copy the other two seals and feed himself. This is how seal mothers in the wild teach their young to feed. They abandon them on the beach until they're so hungry that they start hunting for food themselves. The system seems to have worked for millions of years, so I could only hope it would work for Sulky now.

It wasn't going to be easy to carry the adolescent seals out to the pools. We began by encouraging them onto a blanket, then two people picked up the four corners, making a convenient seal-carrying bag. Everything went well and even Crockett, who needed four people to carry him, was as quiet as a mouse for the short journey to his pool.

But true to his name, it was Sulky who played up. Halfway past the fox and badger pens, he ripped his way out of his bag and flopped onto the grass.

"Leave him!" I shouted, worried that somebody might get bitten. I needn't have worried, everybody scattered as Sulky flopped his way towards the deer sheds. Even though seals can't walk, they can get up quite a speed by simply flopping along. Suddenly, I realised that if Sulky did get into the deer shed area, it would be very difficult to move him. Thinking fast, I grabbed a broom and managed to divert him back onto the path that led to the pool.

Sulky hated not getting his own way and took his feelings out on the end of my broom, but slowly he was heading for the pool enclosure. After about ten minutes, I'd managed to turn him into the gateway, when he spotted the other two seals in the pool. He made a headlong dash and flopped into the water, sending a tidal wave into the field next door. Good old Sulky, he still had to have the last word. He surfaced in the middle of the pool and blew a big, watery raspberry in my direction.

It was a whole week before Sulky decided to start eating for himself. Just to celebrate, he ripped the lining of the pool with his fearsome teeth, leaving the three seals trying to swim in five centimetres of fishy water! It took ten men to move the old pool lining, with three very fat seals lying in the middle! This time, I made sure we replaced it with a double-strength liner, just in case Sulky got any more destructive ideas.

From now on, we needed to concentrate on feeding the seals to get them as fat as possible, ready for their release.

For the next few months life around the seal

pools was quite peaceful. The only change was when we allowed Crockett, who was now enormous, to come into the pool with the other three, so that they could all practise their seal skills together.

All four of them were gaining a lot of weight, and soon the time came for us to release them. Our friend David, who'd brought the seals to us, arranged everything, including the two boats which were to meet us in Norfolk. When he saw the seals, David couldn't believe that they were the same weak, sad animals he'd rescued all those months ago. Now our four seals were big enough to be released into a large colony of other seals at Blakeney Point, only this time, they had to be transported in two vehicles. They had grown so much, we'd also had to make much larger cages to carry them in.

We got to Blakeney in Norfolk without

any problems, but we were greeted with pouring rain and a force eight gale so we all got soaking wet as we loaded the cages onto the boats.

We clambered aboard, falling over each other as we left Blakeney, towing a second boat behind us. There was no cover at all on our boat, and going out to the Point, we were drenched by the seaspray as well as the rain. The boat was tossed from one wave to the next the whole way, but the captain stood firmly at the tiller, as if the sea was as calm as glass.

Finally, after what seemed like an endless trip, we beached on the Point and waded ashore. Our first job was to get the cages off the boats. When our backs were turned, one of them began to float off on the tide, complete with a seal inside! I jumped into the sea fast, to grab the cage and avoid a disaster. Though the rain poured down and we were being lashed by the wind and seaspray, it was wonderful being out on that lonely, wild beach with the local seals bobbing about in the waves, their heads up looking at us.

Our seals seemed to feel the same way and didn't need any encouragement to leave their cages. Except one of them – you've guessed it, Sulky – who turned round and tried to get back into his cage! But soon they were all flopping into the waves and disappearing under the angry surf. Only Crockett surfaced twenty metres out to turn and look back at us on the beach. Then he made up his mind and was gone, back into the pounding sea, his rightful home.

On our journey back by boat, we tried to see which of the bobbing seals' heads looking at us might be one of ours. But it was

impossible to tell – they all looked the sa
After that, we were very quiet because, although we'd had a hard summer looking after them, we were all sad to see Crockett, Silky, Tom, and especially Sulky, go. Although we'll miss them, at least they're back in their proper habitat... and free.

ight Visitors

St. Tiggywinkles has to be open twenty-four hours a day to take in casualties. Many birds and other animals are only out and about during the hours of darkness, and when they have accidents they usually arrive at the Hospital in the middle of the night. They're often brought in by police officers who always seem wide-awake and cheerful no matter what time it is!

It was at that almost eerie time of three in the morning when the latest night-time patient arrived. A long ring on the doorbell shook me out of bed. Staggering down the stairs I could just make out two police uniforms through the glass of the door.

"Sorry to get you up," said the police woman apologetically, "but we were on a blue-light call when we thought we saw something white, crash into the side of the car."

The other officer added, "We're not allowed to stop while we're on a blue-light emergency, but on our way back we looked, and found this bird."

He handed me a cardboard box. When I peered inside, I saw the most beautiful barn owl lying quietly on the bottom, with its wonderful brown mottled back feathers rising and falling as it breathed.

"Well, it's certainly not dead," I told them.

"Can you do anything to help it?" asked the police woman. "We feel so guilty."

"It doesn't look too bad. But I'll need to check it over," I said, trying to put her mind at ease.

Just then, Sue came down to join me and offered the two police officers a cup of coffee.

"We're still on duty, thank you, but can we phone you tomorrow, to see how he's getting on?" asked one.

"Of course," I nodded. "You know our number."

Taking Barney, as we call all barn owls, across to the Hospital, I could see that his eyes were closed but his breathing still seemed very regular. This meant that he'd probably been knocked unconscious. In the Triage Room, where we check in all our new patients, I lifted him out and checked his wings for any broken bones. I noticed his face, chest and underneath were pure white, which meant he was definitely a male barn owl and, like all his species, is very rare in this country. His long legs, also covered with white feathers, ended in enormous, razor-sharp talons that he would normally use to catch his prey and to attack me if I picked him up! But although his legs weren't injured, he was still unconscious and didn't realise that I was handling him.

There didn't seem to be any other injury, apart from concussion from the bang on his head as he'd flown into the police car. Now I needed to give him some medicine to reduce any swelling there might be inside his head. While he was still unconscious, I took the opportunity to give him his injections. Then I settled him down for the rest of the night in a warm hospital cage fitted with its own oxygen supply. This oxygen would also help him recover from any serious head injury.

Owls are lucky. They have a very dense covering of feathers over a surprisingly small head and body. Often, when they do get hit by cars, the thick cushion of feathers prevents any major injuries. Barney was just as lucky and, in the morning, he was standing up trying to look as though he didn't have a hangover! Just looking at his deep, brown eyes, hooded by the light-blue third eyelid that these birds have, I could almost feel his headache. It's a pity you can't give birds a headache pill like humans take.

By the evening, Barney had fully recovered and was behaving like a normal barn owl - not being very friendly. If you looked into his cage, he would bring his head forward and sway from side to side, staring at you all the time and hissing like a snake. If anyone put their hand in, those razor-sharp talons, on legs that seemed to be twice as long as you thought, would flash out fast and grab unwary fingers.

I've been caught many times before, so I was very careful not to get within striking distance when I put food into Barney's cage. In the wild, Barney would catch small animals, like field mice and voles, but at St. Tiggywinkles we obviously couldn't give him *live* animals to eat. Instead, we bought frozen substitutes from the butcher. The food didn't look very tasty, and I left Barney hissing at his breakfast. If I could get him to eat, it wouldn't be long before I would be able to release him.

Barney didn't even look at the food that day, but by the following morning it had all gone. This was good news, but it was even more exciting when overnight Barney brought up a pellet. All birds of prey – owls and hawks – eat animals whole, then the bits of fur and bone they swallow, are collected in their stomachs and spat out as a pellet. A pellet is like a very small sausage. If it's soaked in warm water, it breaks down into different parts and this told us just what Barney had been eating in the wild. It also showed that Barney's digestive system hadn't been injured in the accident.

So far, so good. When people suffer head injuries, hospitals can carry out a brain scan with very sophisticated equipment. If there are any signs of brain damage doctors can often operate to relieve the problem. Unfortunately, there are no such things as brain scans for birds, we just have to watch and wait to see if the bird recovers normally. In Barney's case, this meant keeping him in our Bird Intensive Care Unit for a week and getting Dr John to check his eyes, just in case there was any damage to the minute blood vessels at the back of them.

Barney managed to sail through all our examinations. During the week, he continued to eat well, bringing up more pellets and even attacking the volunteers as they cleaned out his cage every day! He was definitely ready to go outside.

In an outside aviary, Barney could get used to the weather conditions again and, by dive-bombing volunteers, he could exercise those muscles that had become stiff after sitting in a cage for a week. Then, when I felt happy with his progress, I could just open the end of his aviary and he could fly off if he wanted to. Meanwhile, we would carry on putting food in the aviary, just in case he needed an easy meal.

On that first night, with the door open, Barney woke up, stretched, looked at the opening and was gone, like a silent, giant white butterfly, into the darkness and over the fields. Watching him go, my only worry was whether he was really fully recovered. Would he realise that he could still come back and find an easy meal in the aviary if he needed to? I thought I would never see him again.

There was no sign of Barney for the next two nights and I was gradually convinced that he had gone for good. On the third night, as I was carrying a deer casualty down to a shed, a totally silent white ghost flew over my head, almost making me drop the deer. The 'ghost' flew up to a point behind the bright security light, so there was no way I could see what eerie creature had come to haunt me.

I ran to the shed with the deer and closed the door behind me, just in case... Then, when the deer was settled, I peered out foolishly, only to be surprised again. This time I could see it was a barn owl sitting on the shed looking at me, swaying his head just like Barney used to. Then I realised it *was* Barney and that he was the 'ghost' that had flown over me. I hadn't heard him because barn owls have special feathers which enable them to fly as silently as a 'ghost'. Perhaps he was hungry and had come back looking for his easy meal...

As I ran up to the Hospital to get him some food, I wondered where he'd been for the last two nights. Perhaps he hadn't been able to catch any food? Maybe he'd been trapped somewhere? I had no way of knowing. All I knew was that here was a barn owl, following me up the path, wanting food.

I called to Sue and gave her some food to offer to Barney, but when we went outside again, he had gone. We decided to leave the food out anyway but just then, out of the corner of my eye, I saw the white 'ghost' floating across the grass.

"Quick, Sue," I said, "throw some food onto the path!"

Almost before the food had touched the ground, Barney had swooped on it, looked up and then flown once more into the darkness, his meal clutched in fierce-looking talons.

Sue and I waited for hours for him to come back, but we didn't see him again that night. Once more he'd gone, apparently to his own secret hiding-place.

The following evening, we had food ready by the door, just in case Barney came back. Then, just as dusk was falling, Denise, one of our supervisors, came running into the Prep Room.

"Barney's back!" she called excitedly, and

we nearly trampled on her as we rushed outside to see.

Yes, there he was, perched on top of the cold room, glistening white in the glare of the security light. I tossed some food onto the path and watched as he seemed to be trying to make up his mind. Then, as silently as ever, he floated down, grabbed the food, hesitated, then 'ghosted' off once more into the darkness.

From then on, every night, just about dusk, Barney would mysteriously appear for his evening meal. He never came back for a second helping and, to this day, we have no idea where he went to roost. There are some derelict barns just across the road and perhaps this is where he slept during the day.

Barney soon became a great favourite with our staff and volunteers at the Hospital.

Every evening, a group of people waited for him to materialise – and they were never disappointed.

Except for one evening when Barney wouldn't come down to get his food. I was wondering why this might be, when a terrible scream out of the darkness told me the answer. We could just make out a tawny owl sitting on a fence post. It seemed to have heard about the free food and was waiting for a hand-out. Barney obviously knew he was there and it's possible he was too frightened to come down.

This situation lasted about five minutes, with Barney looking worried and hopping from foot to foot, while the tawny kept shrieking. I decided I had to do something to change things, so I walked between the two owls. The tawny decided I was too close for comfort and flew off into the trees, still screaming. As soon as the coast was clear, down came Barney, grabbed his food and flew off in the opposite direction.

The tawny did return much later, but was never as bold as Barney. He only came down for food when nobody was around and all the lights were off. But it seemed as though the presence of the tawny had affected Barney and made him change his habits. Now he started roosting in the aviary during the day and took to waking up and coming for food long before it got dark. The tawny owl kept his distance, still only coming much later in the evening.

The two of them never did meet again. But there was one night when we thought the tawny owl had startled Barney. The first thing we knew was that Rover, one of our rescued Cavalier dogs, started barking furiously at something in the kitchen. I thought that most likely it was a mouse but, when I went in, there was Barney, sitting on top of the kitchen cupboards and not taking the slightest notice of Rover's barking. Of course when he saw me, he tried to fly away, and as owls are not very clever, he'd forgotten how he'd got in. He panicked a bit and fluttered against the window, so I caught him and put him back amongst the trees in the garden.

Luckily, he never tried to get into the kitchen again, and went back to his old ways of waiting outside for his early meal.

This went on for weeks, and his visits became a ritual with even visitors to the Hospital waiting around to see him. Then, one evening, there was a tremendous thunderstorm and torrential rain. It seemed to go on for hours and I could see no sign of Barney. I began to get worried because barn owls don't seem as 'waterproof' as other birds. I only hoped that he'd have enough sense to take cover.

I needn't have worried. The next day I got a phone call from a local factory construction site – the builders had spotted a barn owl fast asleep in the roof. I wondered if it could be Barney. I soon found out because, as the factory was to be a food processing plant, they asked me if I would go and remove the bird. It took me quite a time to catch the owl, but as soon as I got back and showed it into Barney's old aviary, it flew straight up to the roosting box and went to sleep. It really was Barney, and here he was, back home again.

Barney still comes to us for his easy meal every evening. I know we're all going to be very sad if he decides finally to go somewhere else and 'ghosts' off into the darkness for the very last time.

Wilf, the Smallest Badger in the World

Badger cubs are always born in February or early March. By July they look like proper badgers and weigh between six and eight kilos – almost as big as full-grown, adult badgers.

That was why I had such a shock when, last July, Wilf was brought into St. Tiggywinkles. Usually, when a new patient arrives, Lisa only calls me if there's a problem. When Wilf arrived, she was obviously upset and came looking for me straightaway, even though I was right down at the bottom of our field, releasing some garden birds.

"Les!" she called, "I've got this badger in and he's all wrong, somehow. Can you come and have a look at him for me?"

"Sure, no problem," I replied. "What's the matter with him?"

"I don't know," she said, walking towards me looking puzzled, "but he just seems all wrong."

I knew that if Lisa was worried, the badger must really be in a terrible state. All the way back to the Prep Room, where we carry out our examinations, she just kept repeating, "It's all wrong. It's impossible. It can't be a badger..."

I didn't know what to expect, but as I hurried into the Prep Room, just like Lisa, I couldn't believe my eyes. On the examination table was a bundle of towels, and lying curled up in the middle of them was what looked like a dirty badger toy. This toy was alive but only just. Its tiny eyes were half-closed and its mouth was hanging open and full of dirt, as though he'd been trying to eat the ground of the woodland he was found in. He was very cold and shivering and he whimpered quietly as I picked him up. There was nothing of him, I could hold him in one hand. He must have been five months old, because this was July, but he was only as big as a two-month-old badger.

He was so small I couldn't weigh him on the badger scales and had to use the one we keep for weighing hedgehogs. He weighed in at two kilos, the size of a fat hedgehog.

He looked as if he was going to die, so we had to act quickly if we wanted to save his life. We're used to animals in this sort of condition, so everybody knew what to do when I called out my instructions:

"Right," I said, "I want an I.V. drip and I want a heat lamp."

"Which catheter?" asked Lisa.

"Let's try a twenty-two gauge," I replied, hoping as I spoke that we could actually save the young badger's life.

Wilf, which is what we eventually called him, was in a severely shocked condition. He was very cold and the blood had stopped flowing to his legs and skin. By putting the catheter into one of the veins in his leg, the I.V. – or intravenous – drip, would push the warm glucose into his blood stream. The heat lamp and the medicine would help open up his blood vessels and get his circulation going again.

It wasn't easy to do this on little Wilf because his veins had collapsed. Eventually, while Lisa held one of his legs, I succeeded.

"Thank goodness for that." I breathed a huge sigh of relief. "Now let him have some more of the fluids."

When that was done, we put Wilf in a warm baby incubator and monitored his progress.

Drip, drip, drip – very slowly, the life-giving fluids ran into his blood system and gradually Wilf got warmer. All through that first day and night, we took turns to sit with him in case he showed any changes. During the second day, he started to come round, but he only thrashed his front legs in the air and kept raising his head and dropping it again. He didn't really open his eyes properly until the third day. By then he'd stopped paddling with his little front legs but he was throwing his head back, as though he'd got something stuck in his throat.

We managed to look down Wilf's throat, but all we found was a lot of dirt that he'd been living on. Very gently, we washed the inside of his mouth and throat. Then Lisa tried to feed him on a bottle of warm goat's milk. He tried to suck on the teat and managed to swallow a few drops, but he kept throwing his head back as though he had no control over it.

Wilf was obviously starving, and longing to eat. But every time he suckled, his head shot back and the milk would spill out of his mouth and splash all over him and us. I wondered how he'd managed to survive for five months. He must have had a very patient mother or he would have starved long ago. Now Lisa had to be as patient as his mother had been.

Every half-hour for the next two days we all had a go at getting Wilf to swallow some milk. Gradually, he did improve, and finally, was managing to swallow most of his feed and only splashing some off on his feeders. We were ready to remove the intravenous drip that had saved his life. All we had to do was make sure his bottle feeds gave him at least one hundred millilitres of fluid every day.

Now Wilf was in a stable condition, it was time for us to check him more thoroughly. We needed to make a decision about whether we thought he was ever going to get better and be able to lead a normal badger's life.

It was obvious that he hadn't grown properly, but this was probably a genetic fault that we couldn't do anything about. In the long run, it would mean that he would never grow large enough to be released and live with other wild badgers. Of course, he could always stay with us but only if he settled down and overcame all his other handicaps. Wilf was obviously a fighter and it

Sulky would not eat his fish…

but Crockett was happy to eat them all!

The four seals really enjoyed swimming in the pools.

Sulky, Silky, Tom and Crockett were ready to go to sea.

Sulky didn't want to go…

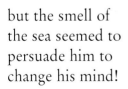

but the smell of
the sea seemed to
persuade him to
change his mind!

Barney was a most handsome barn owl, but he didn't like the kitchen...

he preferred to perch on the rafters above the cold room.

Barney took the food that Sue threw for him.

Wilf was close to dying when he was brought to St. Tiggywinkles...

but started to recover after First Aid treatment.

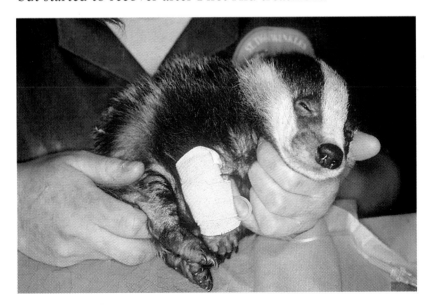

Noisy Willy tried to wreck the filming *and* destroy the aviary.

The *Braer* lay ship-wrecked on the rocks around the Shetland Isles, spewing oil into the sea.

Les held on to the oil-covered otter with both hands –
3 in 1 was a slippery customer.

3 in 1 with his favourite food – fish, fish and more fish!

Godzilla drove Big Bill off *his* island…

With two long slow
flaps of his wings,
Bill soared up and
away… southwards.

Photographs © Les Stocker and Colin Stocker

was up to us to give him a chance.

It wasn't going to be easy, and we all knew that at any moment Wilf might die, or even worse, we might have to put him to sleep. For a start, he had several disabilities that would stop him surviving. The first was his blindness and the fact that he kept tossing his head about. Badgers can't see very well anyway, but there was a chance Wilf's eyesight would come back. So we would just have to wait and see.

Soon, Wilf was getting his head-tossing under control and was beginning to respond to Lisa – taking a bottle and starting to eat some puppy food from her. I even felt sure he was beginning to see, since he now seemed able to tell the difference between darkness and light.

But I was still very worried about his walking. It seemed as though his back legs were fixed solidly at his hips, and though it was impossible to say what had caused this, an X-ray might give us some idea how to make them work again.

In the end, the X-ray didn't show us anything, so after Dr John had given Wilf a thorough examination, all he prescribed was tender loving care, plenty of attention and physiotherapy on his back legs. He promised us that Wilf wasn't in any pain and that he really seemed to love human company. Wilf needed to be able to respond to humans because we would probably never find a badger small enough to live with him. Luckily, Wilf just loved being cuddled and played with. In fact, if he was left alone, he would sometimes sulk and whimper until somebody spoke to him. He was just like a naughty child demanding constant attention and an endless variety of toys.

But eventually, I had to admit that the busy Hospital wasn't the place for Wilf, even though we all loved "the Wilf breaks" we had, when everybody played with him. But little Wilf needed constant companionship of a kind that can only really be given at home.

So one rather miserable day, I arranged for a foster mother, Penny, to collect Wilf and take him home with her, so that she could look after him and give him physiotherapy for his back legs. She could still bring him in to us every couple of days for a cuddle... I mean check-up! But if Wilf didn't settle to life with Penny, we would have to think seriously about what would happen to him in the future.

I needn't have worried, Wilf flourished in his new home. Penny did a marvellous job, and for the next couple of check-ups, I found myself looking at a very happy little badger.

Now he seemed to be able to see as well as any other badger and had put on lots of weight, though the only part of him that looked much bigger was his round tummy. He even seemed to giggle when we rubbed it for him.

In the next few days Wilf tried to stand, but when he tried to walk, his head went backwards and he fell over. But he kept on trying and, knowing what a fighter he was, I was sure he would eventually succeed.

It took another couple of weeks of Penny's patient physiotherapy before Wilf really showed off during "a Wilf break". In front of all his admirers at the Hospital, he got up and walked, not in a very straight line, but at least he'd walked.

From then on there was no holding Wilf back as he began to investigate every blade of grass and anybody's feet, too, if they got in the way. When he was exploring, he looked just like a small tank, with an unruly mop of fur sticking up all over his back. I had never seen such a happy badger.

In spite of this, we were all worried that he might get lonely without any other animal companions. We even thought he might make friends with a miniature pot-bellied pig. But I don't think he ever really felt lonely, because when he was on his own, he played happily, hour after hour, with his toys.

Wilf had many severe disabilities when he first came to us, but he has fought like mad to stay alive and become mobile. Even though we can never really be sure that something else might not go wrong inside his funny little body, for now, he is the happiest of badgers. What Wilf doesn't know is that he's the smallest badger in the world!

Willy the Wrecker

One of the wonderful things about being at St. Tiggywinkles is that you never know what's going to be in the cardboard boxes brought into Reception. But when Tanya Morrison put her cardboard box onto the counter, I could tell from the terrible noise echoing around the room just what kind of bird was inside.

"Drr-drr-drr..." it went, an incessant drilling noise that I knew was going to give all of us a headache before very long. Even the cardboard box was beginning to feel the strain, as the sharp drr-drr-drr beak of the bird finally broke through. It was a woodpecker and it was obviously a master pecker, as now its whole head was poking out of the side of the box.

"What's happened to him?" I asked Tanya, as I pushed his head back inside.

"Drr-drr-drr...!" Tanya couldn't answer because the woodpecker had started all over again.

She shouted, "My cat brought it in through the cat flap! I don't think it's badly hurt, but there is a wound on its back."

"Drr-drr-drr...!" The woodpecker seemed to agree and was nearly through the other side of the box.

"That back wound is typical of a cat injury," I tried to tell her, shouting above the noise. Woodpeckers have chisel-like bills which they use to bore into trees, looking for insects. "He'll need a course of antibiotics, just to make sure," I called.

"Drr-drr-drr...!" The woodpecker was trying to escape again. It would have been nice to let him go, but cats have nasty bacteria on their teeth which can infect and sometimes kill a bird, even if the injury doesn't look serious. Our woodpecker would have to have antibiotics to be on the safe side.

"Let's have a look at him," I suggested, boldly opening the box.

It was a great spotted woodpecker. It had black and white markings, with bright red feathers on its head and under its rump. It was about the size of a starling and a very handsome bird. I'd seen woodpeckers before, of course. They often visit peanut nets under bird tables and we'd had several at the

Hospital. I noticed his funny woodpecker feet, called zygodactyl (that sounds a bit like pterodactyl, doesn't it?) which have two toes pointing forwards and two pointing backwards.

I reached in quickly and caught him round the shoulders. He screamed as though I was about to murder him.

"Drr-drr-drr...!" He started hammering my finger as though it was a branch, which hurt so much that I put him quickly back into the box and shut the lid.

"I'll check him out when he's in a better mood," I told Tanya reassuringly.

"Drr-drr-drr...!" He was at it again as I carried the box down to the Triage Room, where all our new patients are checked in and given first aid.

Lisa got ready to give him his injection of antibiotics, which she would put into the muscles of his chest. But he didn't like this idea and screamed at Lisa.

"Drr-drr-drr....!" he drilled on her fingers. Lisa was so surprised she nearly dropped him, so we decided that she should hold him while I had a go at giving him his injection.

"Drr-drr-drr...!" Now he was attacking my syringe full of antibiotics, but somehow I managed to hold on and give him his life-saving injection.

At last we'd finished and Lisa took Willy the Woodpecker, as we'd called him, down to the Bird Intensive Care Unit, where we have a special recovery cage set up for woodpeckers. Instead of perches across the cage, a woodpecker cage is fitted with logs standing on end so that the birds can hang on the side of them. This is how woodpeckers like to hang on to tree trunks in the wild.

All the way down the corridor to the Bird Unit, I could hear Lisa hissing, "Stop that" or, "Don't do that" as Willy tried to hammer into her fingers.

In his cage, we'd lined up loads of tasty woodpecker food; maggots, mealworms and big fat, waxworm grubs. But was Willy interested? No. All he wanted to do was chisel into things.

"Drr-drr-drr...!" he drilled, having a go at the mini tree trunks.

It was a relief to be able to shut the Bird Unit door, so that his non-stop hammering soon became an echo in the distance.

We thought we'd solved our problem with Willy but, on the following day, we were filming more of our television series, *St. Tiggywinkles*, and television producers demand absolute silence. None of us had reckoned on Willy's latest trick.

"Quiet please!" shouted the producer.

"Camera running," said the camera man.

"And action!" called the producer to me and Lisa handling a fox cub.

"DRR-DRR-DRR...!" went Willy, louder than ever, nearly blowing the sound recordist's earphones off. Willy had discovered he was in a metal cage and hammering the cage made far more noise than some old piece of wood.

"Cut!" screamed the producer.

"Oh, sorry, that's just Willy," I told him, trying to stop Lisa giggling.

"I thought it was Ringo Starr," piped in Tiggy the puppet.

"Can't you shut it up?" glowered the producer, not laughing at Tiggy's comment.

Still smiling, I walked to the Bird Unit and put a large towel over Willy's cage. Now, hopefully, he would think it was night-time and go to sleep. Peace at last! We managed to finish the bit of filming without any more interruptions from Willy.

Later that day, the producer, in a far better mood, thought it would be a good idea to film a woodpecker doing his 'stuff'. And, of course, Willy didn't need any prompting.

"Drr-drr-drr... !" he went, time and time again for the camera, until the poor sound recordist was nearly deafened.

For two more days we endured Willy's non-stop hammering and then I thought he was fit enough to go outside. I can't remember ever being so happy to see an animal moved. I'm sure that even the tawny owls in the Bird Unit were smiling, relieved as I took Willy out, still hammering on my poor fingers.

When we originally built the Hospital I had asked the builders to erect one of the convalescence aviaries around a giant dead tree stump. I thought this would be ideal for woodpeckers who love nothing better than bashing away at old decaying wood. After all, old trees are where woodpeckers dig out and build their nests. I should have known Willy would be different.

With one last scream and attack on my fingers, Willy flew off into the aviary and surveyed his new drumming kit. The giant stump looked inviting but Willy, as awkward as ever, flew straight past it onto one of the uprights holding up the aviary.

"Drr-drr-drr...!" He was off again.

Surely even Willy couldn't damage our beautiful aviaries. After all, they were built of very strong timber, ten centimetres wide by seven-and-a-half centimetres thick. But I wasn't going to take any chances and I'd put in a few more old logs, some apples and tempting dishes of maggots, mealworms, and waxworms hanging on to the wire mesh.

But Willy was having none of it.

"Drr-drr-drr...!" Didn't he ever get exhausted by his own drilling?

The following morning, before dawn, I went outside to check on a badger, and I could still hear him.

"Drr-drr-drr...!"

I was beginning to worry about how much damage he might be doing, and decided to check things out. My fears were justified. One of the aviary uprights was now only half as thick as it was before, and even as I stood there, Willy flew to another upright and began again.

"Drr-drr-drr...!"

The situation was serious, but over breakfast I had a brilliant idea of how we might stop Willy doing any more damage. When we'd been building the Hospital, we'd had loads of square plastic moulding that we'd used to cover water pipes. If I nailed this over all the uprights in the aviary, Willy wouldn't be able to cling on to the wood, and he wouldn't be able to hammer it either!

When I went in to do my own hammering, Willy screamed at me. He must have known that I was stopping his fun. He even flew to the old tree stump and started pecking away.

"Doh-doh-doh-doh..."

It sounded much quieter in the rotten wood of the stump. I thought I'd got some relief for the next twenty-four hours, but then I heard Willy again.

"Drr-drr-drr...!"

I nearly flew down to the aviary myself. Willy seemed fed up with his old tree stump and was now hanging upside down, bashing away at the beams that held up the roof of the aviary. Suddenly, I knew he had to go!

"Right!" I shouted at him like a lunatic. "You're going, today!"

He'd obviously completely recovered from the cat attack and I think now he was telling me, by his non-stop hammering, that he was ready to go back to the wild.

It's always good to see a bird released into the wild again, and nothing was going to give me more pleasure than taking Willy out and letting him go into some poor, unsuspecting wood.

Easier said than done! More screams and sore fingers later, I got him into a carrying case for the short journey up into the Chiltern Hills – perfect woodpecker country.

All the way there, he did his best to give me a headache, as he hammered on the plastic carrying case. Then, when I found a nice glade and opened the case, he promptly flew to an old silver birch tree and began.

"Drr-drr-drr...!"

At last Willy was happy and so was I, and

as I walked away I heard, "Drr-drr-drr..............!" fading into the distance, thank goodness!

3-in-1

When the giant oil tanker, *Braer*, was shipwrecked on the rocks around the Shetland Isles, many thousands of seabirds were put in danger. But it wasn't just birds. I got a phone call asking if we could send a small team to rescue any otters that might have got caught in the millions of tonnes of oil that were gushing from the sinking ship.

My wife, Sue, and I, together with Dr John Lewis, our vet and otter expert, and volunteers Wincey, Chris and Roger, packed our bags and flew off to Shetland, the most northerly part of Britain. We had arranged to meet Paul there, a volunteer from Skye, who'd hired a battered old minibus for us to use around the island.

We all managed to meet up at Shetland's tiny airport, even though the hurricane that was blowing had made landing extremely difficult!

We gave our minibus a big push to get it started and eventually, as it grew dark – in the Shetlands, at that time of year, it gets dark at three o'clock in the afternoon – we set off on the crazy island roads towards our base. We were to live in a small hamlet, called Hillswick, which was sixty miles further north.

Hillswick itself was set in a small bay. The village had one shop, a pub, a wooden hotel, a derelict woollen factory and about six cottages. All round the hamlet were dozens of sheep, living off the seaweed on the beaches.

We didn't see any otters during our first week on Shetland. But in between searching the beaches for any creature that might need our help, we set about trying to turn the derelict woollen factory into an acceptable clinic for otters.

The beaches themselves were in a terrible state. They were covered in thick, greasy black oil which we began to taste in our mouths. The sea was a horrible shade of brown and the hurricane, which was still blowing, meant that we only had four hours of murky daylight to carry out our search each day.

To begin with, we found hundreds of dead seabirds, all black with oil. But we also managed to rescue seventeen alive and give them first aid. We passed these on to the bird centre in the south of the Islands, where they had another two-hundred-and-fifteen seabirds in a similar condition.

Our Dutch friends, from The Zeehondencreche in Holland, were there to rescue seals. They were sharing Hillswick with us and by the end of the first week they'd rescued six seals, but we hadn't come across any otters.

We began to feel puzzled and worried, because Shetland has more otters than anywhere else in Britain, and most of these live in the sea. We just couldn't begin to guess where they might be. Surely they couldn't all have died in the oil spill? We continued our search.

On Sunday, a week after we'd arrived, John, Chris and Roger had to return home. Sue and I felt very lonely standing at the tiny airport watching their plane take off into the hurricane. Sue even cried a little; we were both feeling a long way from home, and hated seeing the effects of the oil and the hurricane destroying such a wild and wonderful island and so many of its seabirds.

But a few hours later, we were cheered up by the arrival of more volunteers who'd flown in to join our team. First we saw the familiar face of Graham, from Surrey, who was always laughing and joking, and together with Gary, Trevor and Ed, they made the sixty miles back to our base a much happier trip.

The otter clinic was now completed and we could all spend more time on the beaches searching for casualties. The hurricane continued to rage, making conditions quite dangerous. Any one of us could have been knocked over into the mountainous seas. But everybody survived, in spite of the bitter cold. We kept ourselves wrapped up in waterproof clothing and boots, with balaclavas covering our faces. We must have looked like some weird bank robbers as we piled out of our battered old minibus, leaning into the wind, with only our eyes showing through the slits in our balaclavas.

We never gave up hope of rescuing more casualties and on our second full day of searching, I spotted our first otter, covered in oil blown off the sea. He was trying desperately to eat a fish coated in oil, another victim of the disaster.

"Graham!" I gasped through my teeth, trying to be heard above the noise of the wind but not wanting to frighten the otter.

Graham turned towards me and, seeing the situation, knew exactly what we had to do. He began to make his way along the oily beach, parallel to the sea, while I approached the otter along the top of the sand dunes. Oblivious of our presence, the oil-coated animal was still trying to crunch his way through a disgusting dinner.

Quite suddenly, the otter looked up, saw me and immediately started to run along the beach, but he was very slow and weak and kept falling over. Graham managed to steer him away from the hole in the sand dunes where he seemed to live and eventually, slipping over on the oily rocks, he thrust his large net over the otter's body. If the otter had escaped, there's no doubt that he would soon have died.

The otter, who we later named 3-in-1 because he was such an oily, slippery customer, certainly didn't want to be caught. Weak as he was, he still managed to spit and snarl as we moved him from the net into a sack for the hike back to the minibus.

Once back in the calm of the woollen factory and out of the wind, we started to examine 3-in-1, and soon began to see just how badly the oil had affected him. Like all wild animals, he could still give someone a nasty bite, so I opened the sack very carefully, while Graham held the otter back with a soft broom. When he was happy, I reached in and took hold of two scruffs of skin behind the otter's head and lifted him out.

"OK," I said to Graham, "I've got him. Can you take his temperature?"

3-in-1 didn't like that idea at all! He snarled and spat, showing us all his needle-sharp teeth that were so good for catching slippery eels and fish. Holding him now was just like trying to hang onto a giant, slippery eel as he tried everything he could to wriggle free. My fingers were starting to ache.

"Hurry up, Graham!" I gasped. "I can't

hang on to him for much longer!"

"Thirty-four degrees Celsius," said Graham at last, having managed to take the otter's temperature.

"That's funny," I said, surprised. "He's hypothermic as well as full of oil."

Hypothermic meant that the otter was very cold and in need of warming up until his temperature reached at least thirty-eight point five degrees centigrade. My fingers were aching so much by now that I knew I was about to let go of 3-in-1. I just couldn't hang on to him for a second longer.

"Aah! Aah! Aah!" I shouted, as I ran to the other room we'd built and almost threw 3-in-1 into his new pen.

We were very proud of our otter pens. We'd made them out of old freezer chests which had had their lids and working parts removed. Willy, a local Shetlander, who looked like a gnome with a bushy beard and pointed woolly hat, had made some wire-mesh lids with string hinges. We'd decided that these would make ideal intensive care pens for any animals we found.

Immediately, 3-in-1 found the bedding box Willy had made, but just flopped down on top of it, taking the warmth from the fan heater I'd switched on. I threw in a couple of dead fish I'd pinched from the seal team and left him to settle in.

In the room next door, we were all sitting down to hot mugs of tea to try and thaw ourselves out, when we heard a strange *crunch-crunch-crunch* coming from the freezer. We crept through and looked into the cage and there was 3-in-1, thoroughly enjoying one of the fishes. His bright eyes looked up at us but he didn't stop crunching for an instant, just waved his long whiskers and let out a slow hiss of disapproval. He was obviously very hungry, which was a good thing, as I'd put the tablets he needed inside the fish. Though he didn't know it, he was taking his medicine.

By now it was mid-afternoon and pitch dark outside, which meant that we couldn't go looking for any more casualties. We made our way back to the hotel to plan our searches for the following day.

I found myself awake well before dawn the next morning. I'd tossed and turned all night, worrying about our otter, and couldn't wait to see how he was. I needn't have worried. Not only had he survived but he'd eaten both the fish and he'd also trashed our otter pen! Freezers are lined with aluminium, which was no match for a determined otter. 3-in-1 had managed to rip out all the aluminium, shredded the polystyrene insulation and was rapidly removing all the old freezer pipes. Obviously our freezer-come-otter pens were not going to work. I had to come up with another idea and I knew just the man to help.

"Willy," I said on the phone to our handyman who was staying at the local pub, "Willy, can you get up here straight away? I need you to make some wooden pens."

"Nay trebble!" said Willy, the first words I'd ever managed to understand through his strong Scottish accent.

In no time at all, Willy had made a wooden chest freezer with string for hinges again.

3-in-1 was nearly through the walls of his existing pen by now, so I had to move quickly. This time he was much stronger, so instead of trying to hold him by the scruff of his neck, I used an animal grasper, a retractable loop on the end of a pole, normally used for catching fierce dogs.

Once again, holding 3-in-1 was like trying to hold on to a very powerful, wriggling eel. After I'd pulled him out of his old pen, I didn't put him into his new pen straight away, but into a large enclosure I'd built out of wire mesh. This way, he would get more exercise and I'd be able to observe him and assess his condition more easily.

3-in-1 thought this was a great game and before I could say "Escaped otter!" he was up and over the wire and running around the room, scattering everything in his path. First went a bucket of wet fish and then a stack of wood that Willy had been using, and then he was up on our table sending cups and teabags flying in all directions! Then he spotted the shelves we'd put up to store all our medical supplies. I could see instantly what he was about to do, but couldn't stop him, as he slithered under the grasper with which I was trying desperately to catch him.

Down came bottles of pills, bandages and instruments all over the floor. Then he headed in Sue's direction. She made a wild grab at him and I shouted "Don't! He'll have your finger off!" and dived in Sue's direction, just managing to slide the grasper over the otter's head and yank him away in the nick of time. Then, finally, I dumped him into his new pen and slammed the lid down.

I don't know who was more out of breath him or me, but that didn't stop *him* diving onto a dead octopus Willy had put in for him to eat. That kept him quiet, while we tidied up the rooms and I rolled up the wire mesh pen. I wouldn't be using that again in a hurry.

For the next three weeks, 3-in-1 continued to eat well. He got stronger and stronger and eventually he was joined by two other otters affected by the oil spill. Nobody managed to find any others, and I only hope they had managed to escape the disaster.

As part of our building programme on Shetland, we converted some old cattle sheds into concrete otter pens. Any other otters that might be found could be kept there until the oil had been cleared from the islands. When we left, the otters were safely in their new pens, with Willy and other local people looking after them.

The following week, Dr John flew back to the island, just to check on the otters' progress and finally hand over their care and release to the people of Shetland.

3-in-1 had taught me a lot about otter behaviour. Knowing him has helped me to look after the other otters we've had since at St. Tiggywinkles.

Big Bill the Heron

It's not unusual to see small birds chasing bigger birds, especially birds of prey, such as kestrels and owls. They make a terrific noise when they're doing this, and since there seems to be safety in numbers, they never seem to be attacked themselves. When they 'mob' another bird, it's usually to chase it away from their nests and babies. You can see why smaller birds take these risks with birds of prey, but why any bird should want to mob a heron, one of Britain's largest birds, is still a bit of a mystery. After all, herons eat mostly fish and amphibians, like frogs and toads, and they have long sharp beaks which they use like daggers.

This was just how I got to know Big Bill. He sounds like a real tough guy, but Big Bill had only been chased by two small crows and he'd ended up cowering inside someone's house.

It was a Mr Harland who'd telephoned us and asked us to help. He needed rescuing nearly as much as Big Bill, as it turned out. It was easy to imagine the heron inside his house, flapping down the narrow passage and knocking over all the ornaments and bellowing out his harsh haa-arnk sound – a heron's warning cry. No wonder Mr Harland was sitting outside on his doorstep, when I arrived, too scared to go back into his own house.

It was very dark in the long passage, and

the only way I could see anything was to use my small pocket torch. I couldn't see the bird in the passage, but right at the other end there seemed to be a black hole which loooked like some sort of cupboard under the stairs.

Quietly, I crept forward and shone my torch into the gloom. The beam wasn't very strong but I could just make out the huddled shape of the heron in the far corner of the cupboard, still shaking after the trauma of being mobbed. Poor old Bill, I was going to have to scare him all over again by crawling right inside the open cupboard to try and catch him.

"Mr Harland!" I called back down the passage. "I need your help. Would you hold my torch so I can see what our heron is doing with that long beak of his?"

Mr Harland wasn't too keen on coming into the cupboard, but he agreed to put one arm in, holding the torch. I crept slowly towards Big Bill, watching his lethal beak all the time – one stab from that and I would have a serious injury.

I reached out and grabbed his beak first.

"Haa-arnk!" Big Bill suddenly let rip and became a whirlwind of flapping wings, battering me and hitting the sides of the cupboard, his long legs dangling and treading thin air. Mr Harland dropped the torch and ran, leaving me completely in the dark!

Somehow I managed not to let go of the beak and pulled Big Bill into a more roomy part of the cupboard. Still on my knees, and holding his beak in my left hand, I felt for his shoulders and finally managed to reach his wings and fold them in until they were under control. But his legs still thrashed around in all directions and it was a bit like trying to cuddle an octopus!

At last, I tucked the whole of Bill and his long legs under my right arm. Still holding tight to his beak I stood up and tried to find the door. I found it all right, but only after banging my head on every stair going up above me as I crouched in the cupboard. I was hanging onto Bill for dear life, and he was honking, flapping and trying to escape.

I wasn't happy, and the heron definitely wasn't happy, but Mr Harland stood smiling at us. I folded Big Bill into a carrying basket, and a look of relief flooded over Mr Harland's face.

Back at St. Tiggywinkles, we had another wrestling match, as I tried to check Bill over for any injuries. His 'haa-arnks' echoed around the Hospital, and anybody passing would have thought I was trying to murder him. In fact he was trying to murder me with his vicious weapon of a beak!

Bill was lucky. Apart from his dented pride he only had two broken feathers, and a black eye where he'd banged himself fleeing down the passage. Nothing too serious, so with some soothing ointment in his eye, I put him into one of the large cages in our Bird Intensive Care Unit.

But he did look miserable! He was all hunched up in the corner glaring at me through his sore eye. Even a bowl of fish didn't make him any brighter, so I decided to leave him in peace to recover his dignity over night.

In the morning, Bill was quite a different bird. He was standing up as tall as my waist and was staring at me, straight along that fearsome beak, as if to say, "Don't meddle with me. I'm a really tough heron!"

I saw that Bill hadn't eaten any of his fish

and I knew that I'd have to grab him once more to try and feed him by hand. Another wrestling match was about to begin.

First, I got some fresh fish from the refrigerator. Then I grabbed his beak again and took him out of his cage. He was much stronger than the day before, and his 'haa-arnks' nearly burst my eardrums! He kicked and flapped but eventually I managed to tuck him neatly under my arm. I forced open his beak with my fingers and, one by one, slipped the fish, head first, into the back of his throat. Luckily, he swallowed every one of them and didn't even cough them back up – one of a heron's favourite tricks.

For three days we went through this daily wrestling match until, finally, on the morning of the fourth day, he had eaten some fish all by himself.

Bill's bad eye had healed beautifully by

now. During one of our wrestling matches I had mended his two broken feathers by glueing on two lengths of old feathers that other herons had moulted. Now he was ready to go outside into one of our largest flight aviaries. Once he was out there, I could watch how well he was able to fly and would soon be able to judge when he would be ready for release.

After another tussle, I got him out to the aviary. When I'd let him go inside I stood back expecting him to fly to one of the higher perches. But not Big Bill! He decided he was going to be awkward and now he'd got his legs, his wings and his dignity back, he just walked to the furthest corner, sat down on his haunches and tried to look as miserable as before. I wasn't worried. I knew what an actor our Bill could be, so I went out of the aviary and left him to his own little tricks.

But I had a trick or two of my own up my sleeve.

Once Bill had seen me go back into the Hospital, I crept to the Staff Room window and spied on him through the closed Venetian blinds. He didn't know I was there of course and, like many wild birds, he waited until nobody was around before he started to relax and behave normally. As soon as the coast was clear, he stood up, shook himself and marched straight over to his food bowl. In six gulps he'd swallowed six herrings. There was nothing wrong with Bill's appetite!

After that, Bill had a bath and a good go at preening his feathers. Soon he began to look his real self again, not at all like the hunched-up creature we saw every time we went near the aviary.

Big Bill carried on teasing tricks like this

the whole time he was with us, but by watching him from the Staff Room, I could see that he was beginning to fly up to the higher perches. I felt that soon he would be ready to go, and when I heard him 'haa-arnking' to other herons flying high above the Hospital, I knew I was right. I decided to release him in two days time.

The day dawned bright and cold. I peered at Bill through the Staff Room window as usual and spotted him standing on the highest perch, preening the beautiful black and white feathers on his chest which always reminded me of a smart waistcoat. I bet he went down well with all the female herons in the neighbourhood!

Bill saw me coming and immediately jumped down into the corner, assuming his usual bedraggled and miserable look again. But I knew he was fine and wasn't going to be fooled by his wily tricks. We went through our normal wrestling match again when I picked him up and carried him out of the aviary.

I had Bill tucked securely under my arm as I walked towards our main waterbirds' pool and put him gently down on the ground, expecting him to fly off straightaway. But not Bill! He walked proudly and sedately round the pool until he found himself coming beak-to-beak with Godzilla, a disabled heron who lived there. Godzilla didn't take kindly to other herons invading his territory, and 'haa-arnking' noisily, launched himself at Bill, his head down and beak stretched out in front of him, determined to take on his new rival. With a 'haa-arnk' of surprise, Bill flew off towards the safety of the island. Godzilla, who couldn't fly, thought he owned the island, and jumped into the water with a loud splash and began to swim out towards it.

Bill stood his ground for as long as his timid nature would allow and then, unable to cope with Godzilla's frenzied whirlwind attack and fearsome 'haa-arnking' any longer, he decided to get away. He lifted his enormous wings and for a brief while seemed suspended in the air, his long legs dangling beneath him. Then, with two long slow flaps of his wings, he soared out over the deer paddocks behind the pool. He flew beautifully, with deliberate slow powerful beats of his great wings, circled back over the Hospital and gradually gained height until he was just a speck in the sky, gliding off southwards.

Godzilla, of course, was triumphant. He'd seen off another heron from his pool and now he could settle back in his domain, lording it over the ducks and swans.